For my sister, Susan Lang-Passaro, who has enough love
to fill the hearts of a million tortoises——plus three.

A portion of the proceeds from the sale of this book will be donated to Galapagos Conservancy, which is dedicated to conserving the unique biodiversity and ecosystems of Galapagos, and Darwin Animal Doctors, which provides free veterinary care to all the animals of Galapagos.

REX IMPERATOR

Hermann Finds Home

©2016 Nancy Lang-Feldman. All Rights Reserved. No part of this publication may be reproduced, stored in a retrieval system or transmitted in any form by any means electronic, mechanical, or photocopying, recording or otherwise without the permission of the author.

Library of Congress Control Number: 2016906023

CPSIA Code: PRT0616A
ISBN: 978-1-63177-684-7

Printed in the United States

Hermann
Finds Home

written and illustrated by **Nancy Lang-Feldman**

My name is Hermann, and I'm a tortoise.

There are lots of different kinds of tortoises: leopard tortoises, gopher tortoises, red-footed tortoises, Hermann's tortoises. Guess what type of tortoise I am!

Right! A Hermann's tortoise!

France

Italy

Spain

Corsica

Sardinia

Sicily

Hermann's tortoises come from the countries near the Mediterranean Sea.

We like a warm and sunny climate.

When I was a baby, a little boy named Wally took me home from the pet store.

I liked playing with Wally's toys,
especially his skateboard.

But Wally preferred playing games I wasn't very good at. I tried to be good at fetch, but by the time I brought the ball back it would be time for dinner!

Wally decided I might be happier playing with other children, so he brought me to school with him.

Boy, was he right!
I had so much fun playing with all the children
at school.

But the best part of school was Susan, the teacher. The moment I saw her I knew I loved her, and I knew she loved me too. One day after all the children went home, she picked me up and said, "I'm going to take you home with me!" I was so happy!

That Friday, after school, Susan put me in a little carrying case she called my tortoise taxi, and we got into her car and drove to her house.

When we got there, she put me in the most beautiful tortoise habitat I had ever seen! It had everything I could want—water for when I got thirsty, food for when I got hungry, a heat lamp to keep me warm, and a log to crawl under when I just wanted some "me time."

Susan would always make sure I had the healthiest food. She would give me the freshest romaine lettuce for my meals, and for a special treat, she would feed me fresh strawberries! Tortoises shouldn't have strawberries all the time, but once in a while, it's okay.

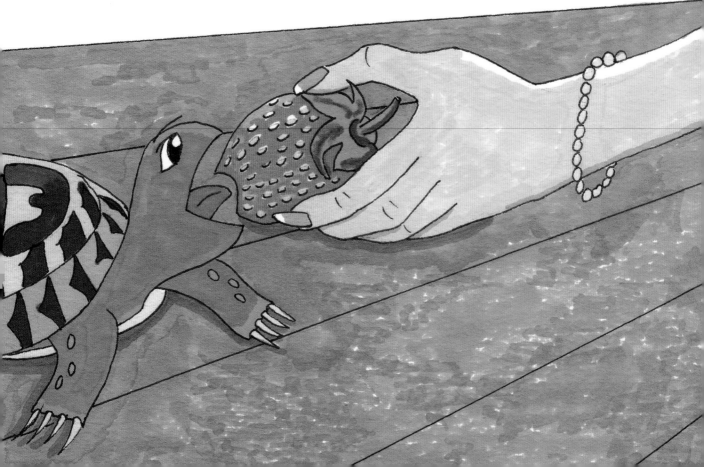

I was as happy as a tortoise could be—school during the week and Susan's house on the weekends! When the weather was warm, we would spend quality time in Susan's backyard, where I could walk around in the grass and soak up the rays of the sun.

When school was out, Susan would take me to her summer job—a day camp, where I had more children to play with! The camp even had a special house where all the small animals slept at night, including me!

Critter Shack

That was my life until one night when everything changed. I had the strangest dream I was shivering, and when I woke up, I found myself on the floor of the critter shack. I couldn't get back into my habitat because tortoises are not good climbers. But I couldn't spend the night on the cold floor!

There was only one thing to do: I had to find Susan! I knew she would tell me how much she loved me and put me back in my nice, warm tortoise habitat. But where did she live? And how would I get there? I would never know unless I tried, so I headed for the door. To my surprise, it was wide open!

How big the world looked! Grass, trees, rocks, ponds, fields! How would I ever find my Susan?

I didn't know which way to go, so I decided to just walk until I found her. Before too long, I came upon a fat, furry animal munching on what looked like one of the cupcakes the campers got at lunchtime.

After years in the classroom, I'd learned a lot, so I knew it was a raccoon!

"Hello there!" said the raccoon. "What's your name?"

"I'm Hermann," I said.

"I'm Ruthie," she said. "How are you this fine evening?"

"Not so well," I said.
"I'm looking for Susan. Have you seen her?"

"Susan, the sparrow?
Why yes, she lives up in that tree with her mate and their three young chicks," said Ruthie.

"No, no!" I cried. "My Susan doesn't have wings or feathers. And she doesn't have fur, except on her head, which is covered with a beautiful golden mane."

"She sounds lovely, Hermann. But I'm sorry.
I haven't seen her," said Ruthie.

I was very sad and disappointed, but I wished Ruthie
a good night and continued on my way.

I walked and walked until I came to a road. I was about to cross when a car sped by so fast I flipped over onto my back. This is a terrible fate for a tortoise because it's very difficult to get back on your feet by yourself.

As I was lying there wondering what to do,
I heard a rustling in the leaves.

It was Ruthie!

"Hermann!" she cried. "You look like you need some help."
And with her front paws, she pushed me back on my feet.

"Thank you, Ruthie! I'm so lucky you found me!"

"I'm glad I could help," she said.

And, once again, we said our goodbyes and
I continued on my journey.

I was sad and tired, and now very hungry, so I decided to munch on some plants. They weren't as yummy as the lettuce Susan would bring me, but everything tastes good when you're hungry!

After my meal I grew sleepy. So I crawled under a pile of leaves for warmth and took a nap.

The next morning when I crawled out, nothing looked familiar. I was horribly lost! I had to face the truth: I might never see my Susan again! I started to cry. At first, just a little, but after a while I just couldn't control myself. I bawled like a big, old baby tortoise, and I didn't care who heard me.

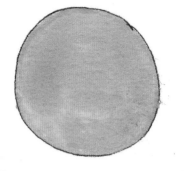

Suddenly, a voice from under a bush asked, "What's the matter?" I told the voice my story and it listened patiently before crawling out. To my surprise, I saw a tortoise that looked just like me!

"Hi, I'm Shelly," she said. "I grew up in a home with a little girl, but she went away to school. Her parents brought me here, and I've been all alone ever since."

"Not anymore," I said. "Now you have me!"

And that's how my new life began. Shelly and I have
been very happy together since we found each other.
We've even had a child of our own,
and we named her Susan!

So, if you see Susan, tell her I still love her and think of
her often. Tell her I miss her, but that I've found a new
home, and she doesn't have to worry
about me anymore.

HERE ARE SOME FUN FACTS ABOUT TORTOISES!

Tortoises are turtles that live on land. While they can't breathe under water, they can stretch their necks up to keep their heads above the water's surface.

Tortoises prefer warm climates. In cooler climates, some species of tortoises sleep through the winter and wake up when the weather warms up. This is called hibernation.

Some species of giant tortoises from the Galapagos Islands can grow as big as six feet long and weigh more than 500 pounds. The heaviest ever was Goliath, who weighed more than 900 pounds!

Some tortoise species can live for more than 150 years! The oldest tortoise ever was Tu'i Malila, who lived to be at least 188! Tu'i Malila was presented to the Royal Family of Tonga by British explorer Captain Cook in 1777 and lived on the palace grounds until 1965.

The most famous Galapagos tortoise was Lonesome George. His species is considered extinct, but scientists recently found some of his close relatives alive and well.

Tortoises are good for the environment because as they walk around on the ground they open up the vegetation and spread seeds so that new plants can grow.

Most tortoises are herbivores, which means they eat plants. Their favorite foods are grasses, weeds, flowers, leafy greens, and fruit. Some of the larger tortoises can survive without eating or drinking for up to a year!

Baby tortoises hatch from eggs. A mother tortoise can lay up to 30 eggs at a time, although some lay only four to seven eggs in a nest. The eggs hatch in two to five months, depending on the temperature, and the babies set out in search of food within a week.

Tortoises are gentle creatures. They settle disputes with other tortoises by stretching their long necks. The tortoise that stretches its neck the highest wins the argument.

Tortoises protect themselves from predators by hiding their legs and head in their shells.

Tortoises may be slow, but they reached the moon before humans. In 1968, a Soviet spacecraft sent tortoises in an orbit around the moon. That's almost a year before two-legged astronauts got there!

About the Author

Nancy-Lang Feldman lives on Long Island with her husband, Rob, and a pond full of goldfish. She and her sisters, Susan and Barbara, always had turtles when they were kids, and they have fond memories of organizing turtle races across their bedroom floor. Not surprisingly, the one named Speedy would always win.